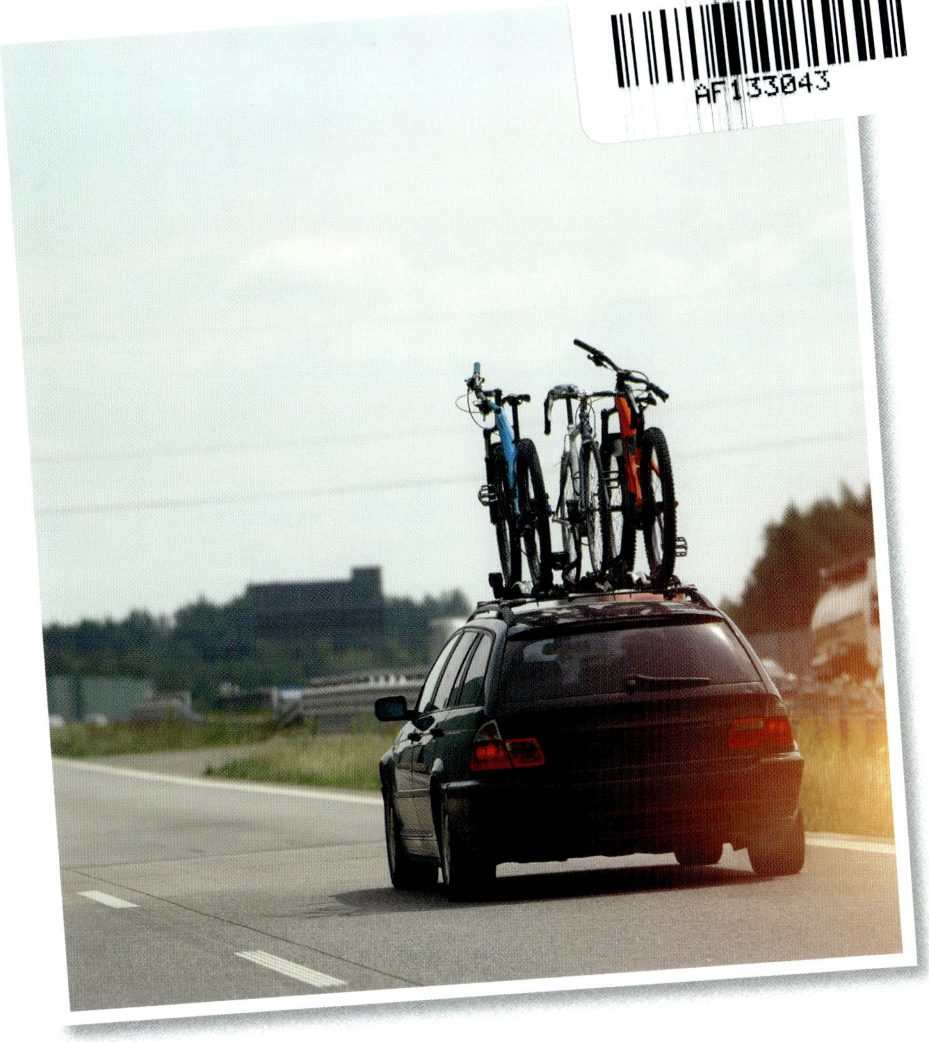

A car

a pickup truck

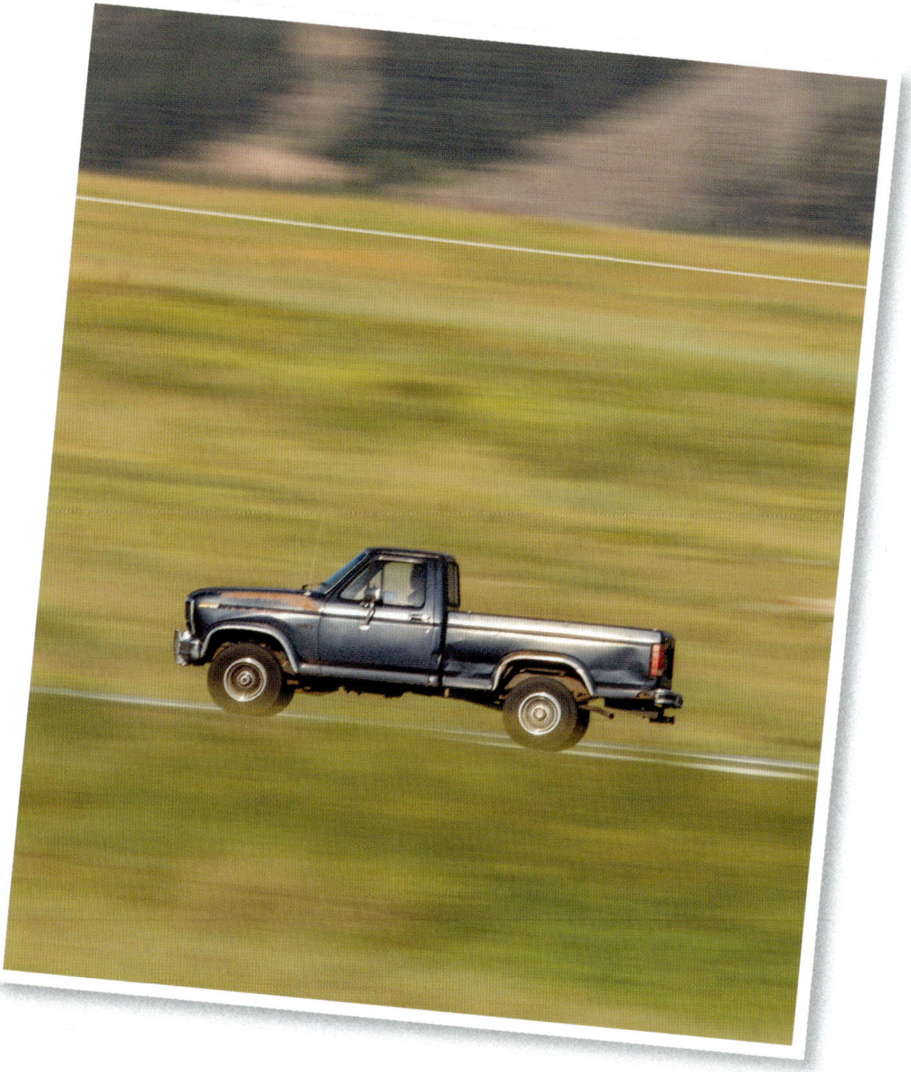

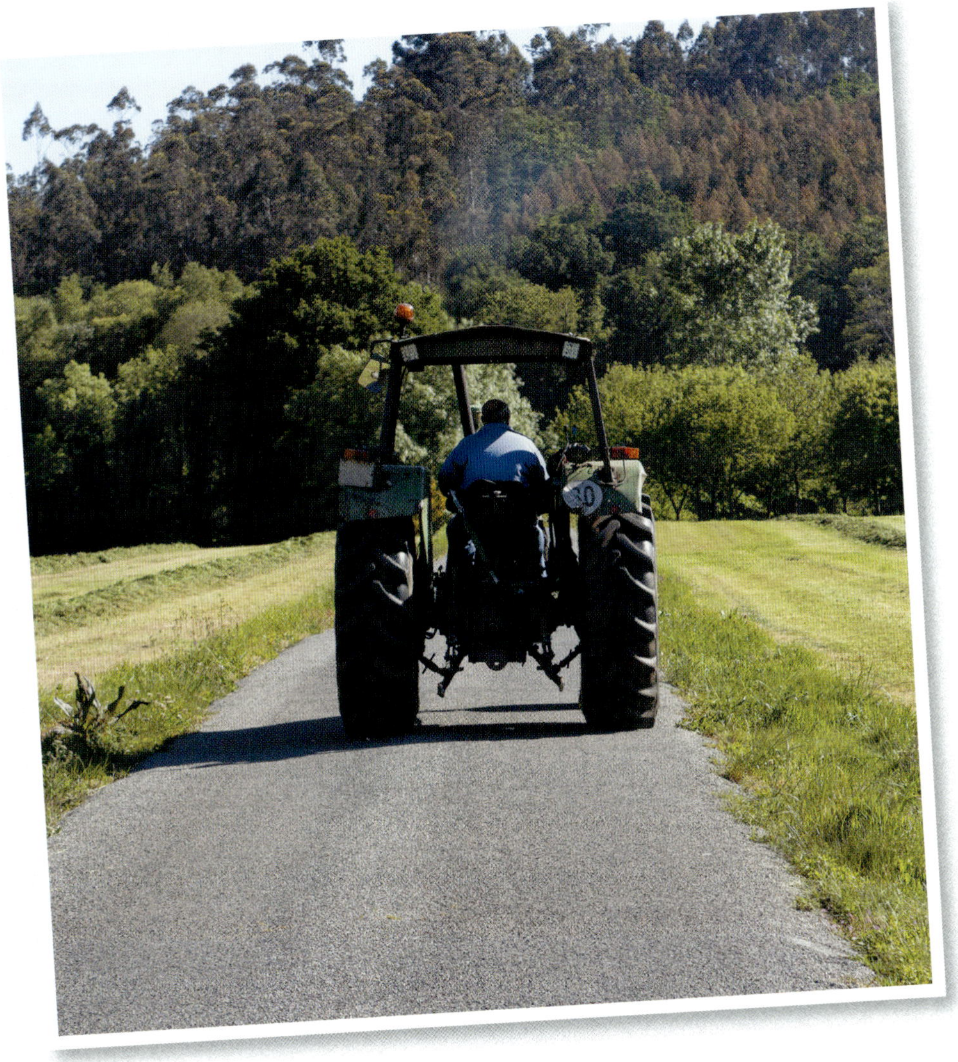

a tractor

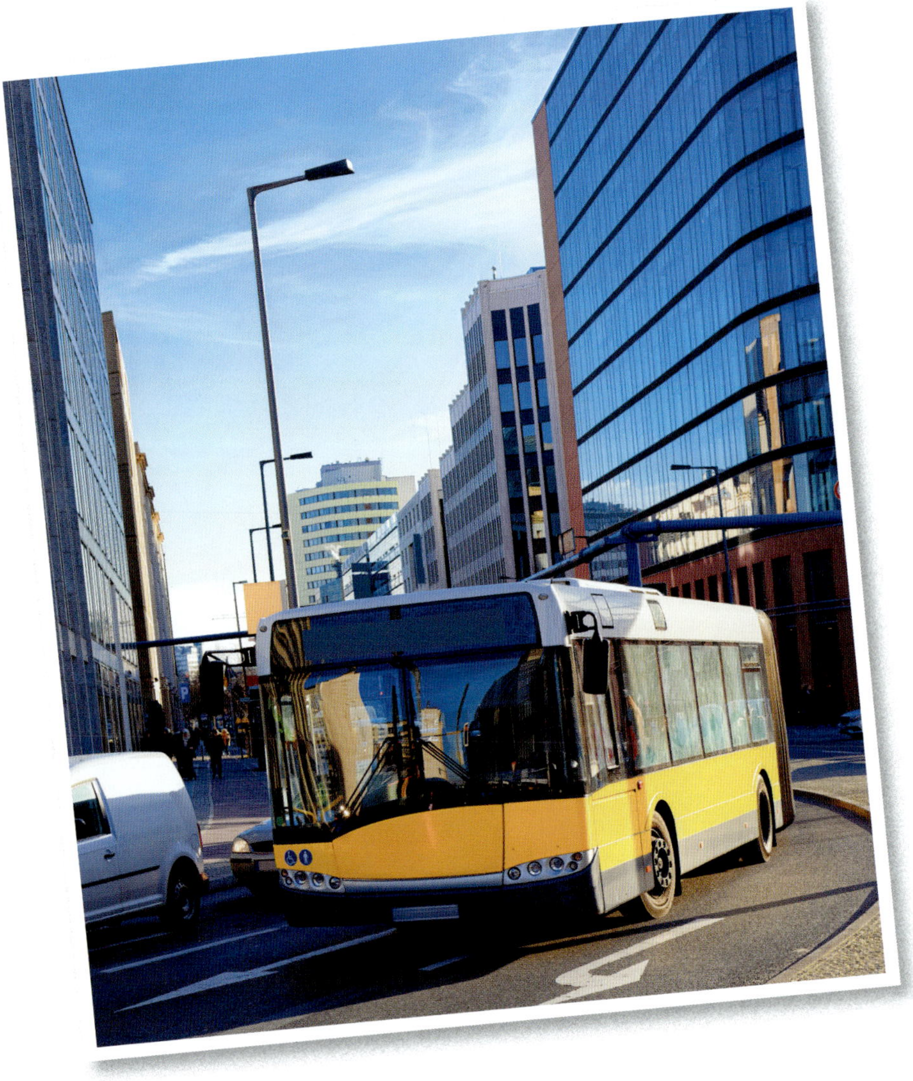

a bus

a van

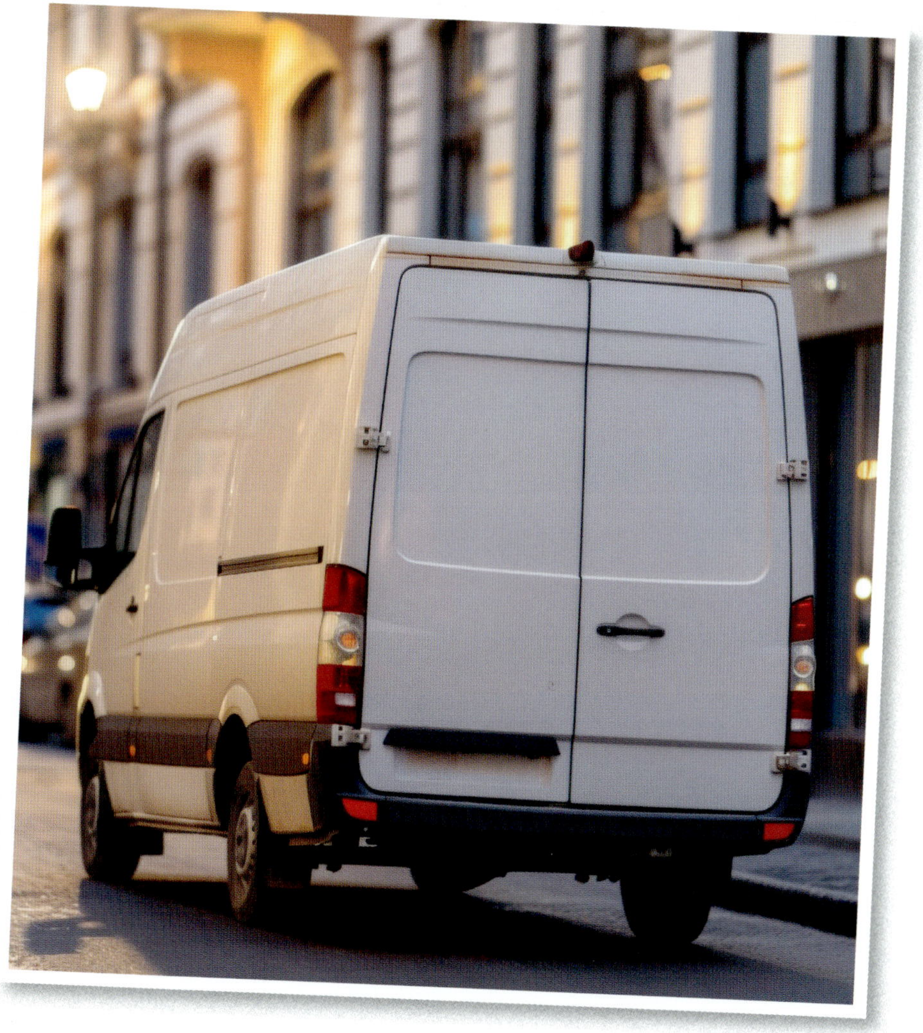

a sports car

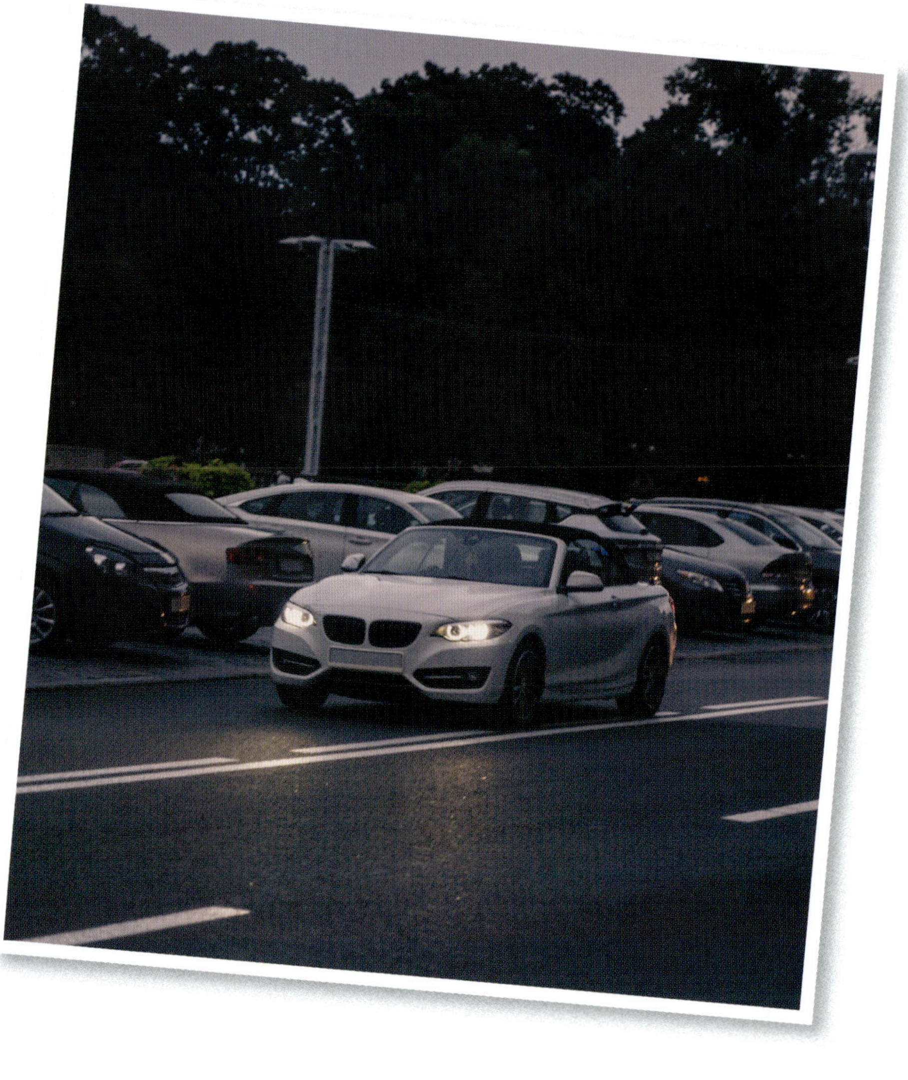

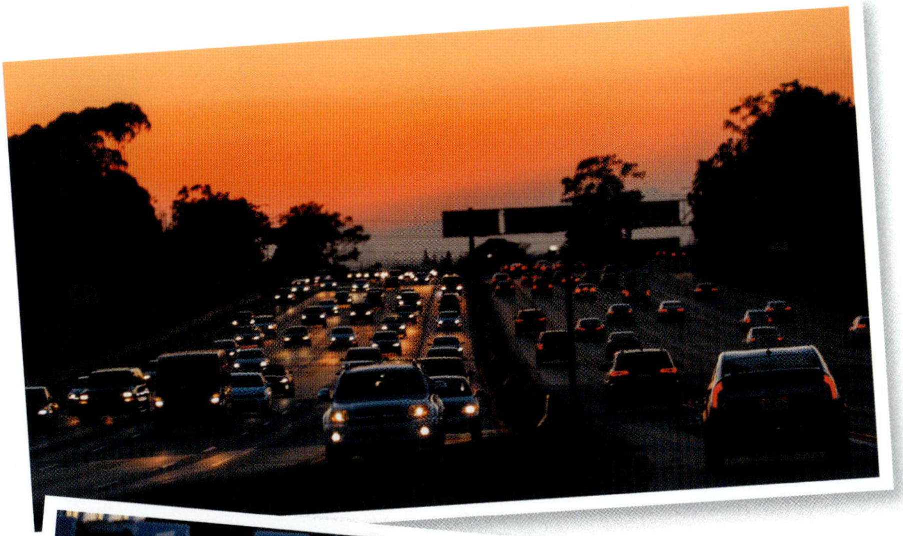

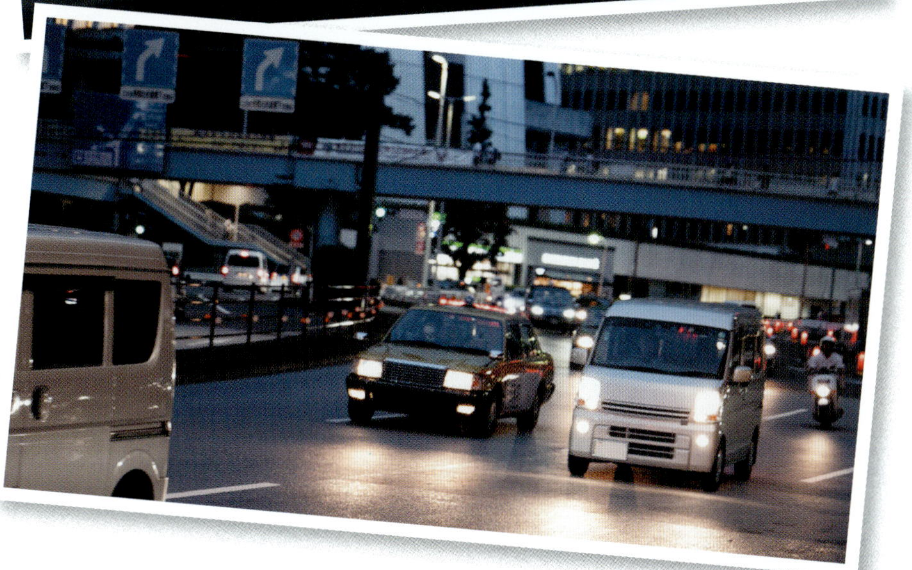

cars, cars, cars

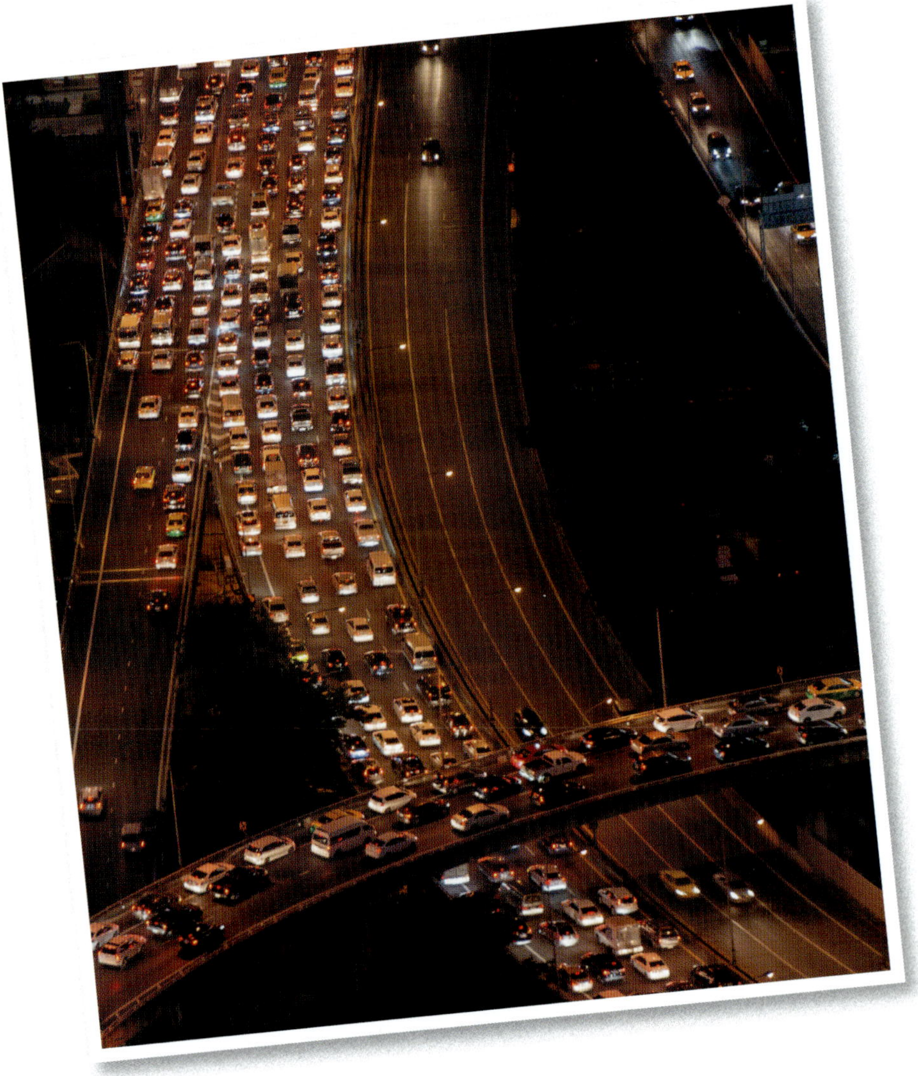

a traffic jam!